# A New Tune A
# Scales & Arpeggios

**Boston Music Company**
part of The Music Sales Group
London/New York/Paris/Sydney/Copenhagen/Berlin/Madrid/Tokyo

Published by
**Boston Music Company**

Exclusive Distributors:
**Music Sales Limited**
14-15 Berners Street, London W1T 3LJ, UK.
**Music Sales Corporation**
257 Park Avenue South, New York, NY10010, USA.
**Music Sales Pty Limited**
120 Rothschild Avenue, Rosebery, NSW 2018, Australia.

This book © Copyright 2006 Boston Music Company,
a division of Music Sales Limited.

Compiled and edited by David Harrison
Cover and book designed by Chloë Alexander
Photography by Matthew Ward
Models: Ben Cartlidge, Matthew Deacon, Martin Hadley, Sasha Haworth,
Chigozie Nri, Joshua Williams and Martin Young.
Printed in the EU

**Your Guarantee of Quality**
As publishers, we strive to produce every book to the highest commercial
standards. The music has been freshly engraved and the book has been
carefully designed to minimise awkward page turns and to make playing
from it a real pleasure. Throughout, the printing and binding have been
planned to ensure a sturdy, attractive publication which should give years
of enjoyment. If your copy fails to meet our high standards, please inform
us and we will gladly replace it.

www.musicsales.com

# A note to the teacher

This book is designed as a general resource, and should by no means be considered a comprehensive overview of scales or arpeggios as required for exams. Each scale and arpeggio is shown in two octaves, with no articulation, no rhythm groupings and no suggested fingerings. Apart from the traditional major and minor scales, this book also includes scales more useful in rock and in jazz, and which are increasingly finding their way into the exam syllabus, such as diminished, pentatonic and blues scales. Scales are set out in order of key signature, with treble clef versions followed by those for bass clef.

The teacher is encouraged to work with the student to devise challenging studies based on any of the scales in this book for fingering, improvisation, ear-training, articulation, sight-reading and general technique.

# A note to the student

Whichever instrument you play, scales and arpeggios will form a significant part of your practice routine. The range of your particular instrument may not be the same as the scales written in this book, but you can tailor them to your individual needs. For exams, your scales will need to be played in a certain way, so make sure you always check the requirements for articulation, range and rhythmic groupings given in your exam syllabus.

At the back of this book, you will find some useful suggestions for new ways to incorporate the scales and arpeggios into your practice schedule. Don't forget: give every scale and arpeggio the same care and attention as you would to any great solo. Listen to the sound you are making, keep a steady tempo and let the instrument sing out!

# Contents

Major scales are a mainstay of Western music, and melodies based on this scale are everywhere. The familiar sequence of *tone-tone-semitone-tone-tone-tone-semitone* should become second nature to the music student. Learn a few major scales by heart, and you'll be surprised how easy it becomes to play a few more just by letting your ear guide you.

The modes of the major scale can almost be thought of as keys-within-a-key. The word *mode* has the same root as the English word *mood*, and throughout history composers and performers have created a particular mood in a piece of music by choosing a suitable mode. Play each mode in turn and make a note of how it sounds. Is it bright? Is it mysterious? Is it unsettled? Play the modes of any major scale simply by starting on a different step of the scale. Try creating a melody using different modes and see where the mood takes you!

Compare the minor scales with the Aeolian mode. The *descending* version of the melodic minor scale is identical to the Aeolian mode, and the harmonic minor is the same except for a sharpened seventh note.  The melodic and harmonic minor arpeggios are identical to one another. Listen out for the characteristic interval of a tone-and-a-half between the seventh and eighth notes of the harmonic minor scale, and notice how sharpening the sixth and seventh notes of the melodic minor is only necessary on the way up.

The *pentatonic* (meaning 'five-note') scale is found in music the world over. The major pentatonic, being the major scale without the fourth and seventh notes, is essential in rock, jazz and folk, while the minor pentatonic (itself a mode of the major pentatonic) is the basis of the blues scale, which is crucial in rock, jazz and the blues. Try improvising a melody using these various scales, and learn to hear how each note relates to every other note of the scale.

How about the 'extra note' in the blues scale that isn't in the minor pentatonic? What effect does it have? If your instrument is capable of bending or sliding from one note to another, investigate the effect this has on different notes. Try *singing* a bluesy phrase and then repeating it accurately on your instrument.

## Chromatic, Diminished & Whole-Tone Scales
## and Arpeggios                                                40-45

There is only one chromatic scale, of course, and it can be started wherever you like. Try grouping it in pairs, and then in threes, and be sure to play it smoothly throughout your chosen range.

The diminished scale is a repeating pattern of semitones and tones, and is useful in rock, jazz, and 20th-century classical music. You could think of the diminished scale as being a chromatic scale with four notes missing – and this helps to explain why there are only three diminished scales in existence. Get used to starting each scale on any of four different notes as grouped in the diminished arpeggios.

The whole-tone scale could equally be thought of as a chromatic scale with every other note missing. Therefore, only two whole-tone scales exist, and each one can begin and end anywhere. Because there is no obvious 'tonic' note, these scales require extra concentration. The arpeggio divides the octave into three equal parts and is known as an *augmented* arpeggio.

## Minor 7 & Dominant 7 Arpeggios                      46-53

The minor 7 is an arpeggio of the dorian mode, and is especially useful in rock and jazz for playing over m7 (minor seventh) chords. Learn to play it up and down, and notice how it differs from the dominant 7 arpeggio. The dominant 7 arpeggio is from the mixolydian mode, and is extremely useful in rock and jazz for playing over 7 chords. Hear how the dominant 7 arpeggio seems to create a tension: which two notes in the arpeggio are responsible for that? And why?

## Practice Tips                                                    54-56

Endlessly plodding up and down boring scales is no-one's idea of fun! This section gives the student a number of ideas for approaching scales and arpeggios with a fresh twist. And this is just the beginning: find your own patterns and exercises, and repeat them in all the different scales you discover. Soon you'll be memorising scales and improving your muscle memory too.

Incorporating scale and arpeggio patterns into your daily practice routine is a great first step to hearing how they work in composition and performance. Above all, take pride in what you do. You could keep a diary to monitor your progress, or you could set yourself weekly challenges. You'll soon notice the difference!

# Major Scale

### G major

### D major

### A major

### E major

### B major

### F♯ major

### C♯ major

**C major**

**F major**

**B♭ major**

**E♭ major**

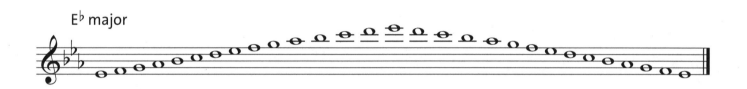

**A♭ major**

**D♭ major**

**G♭ major**

**C♭ major**

# Major Arpeggio

G major

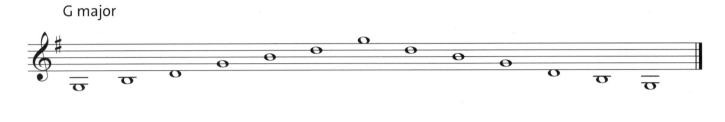

D major

A major

E major

B major

F# major

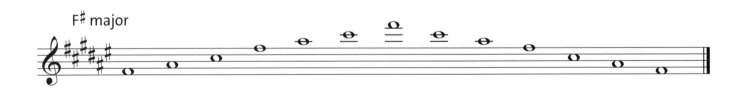

C# major

C major

F major

B♭ major

E♭ major

A♭ major

D♭ major

G♭ major

C♭ major

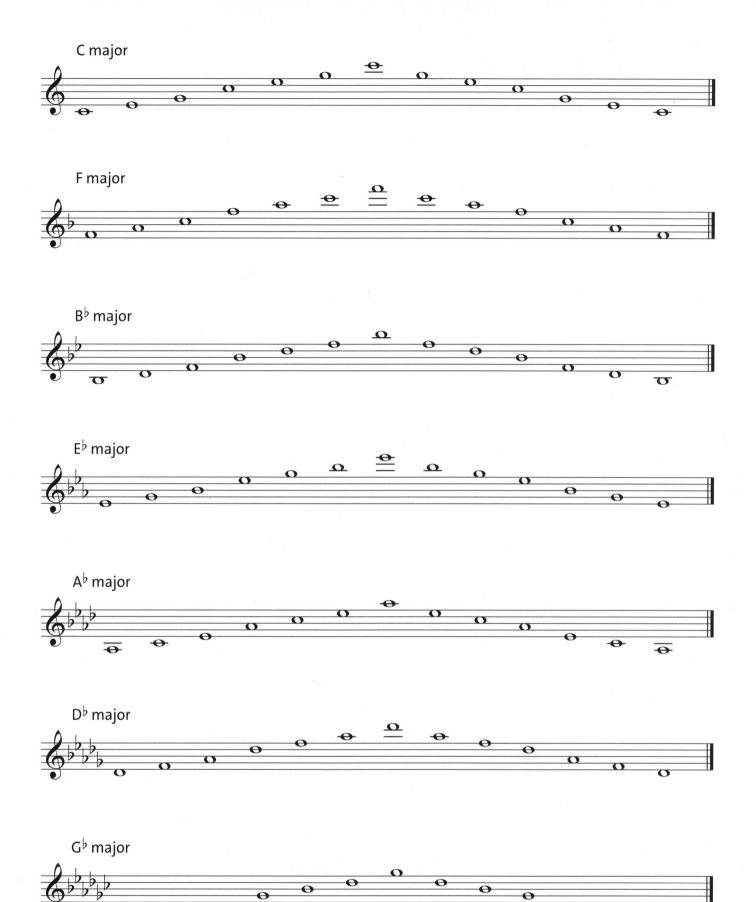

# Major Scale

### G major

### D major

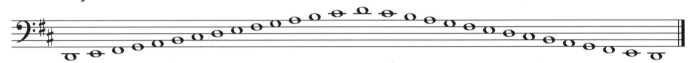

### A major

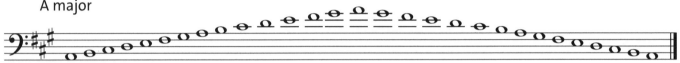

### E major

### B major

### F♯ major

### C♯ major

**C major**

**F major**

**B♭ major**

**E♭ major**

**A♭ major**

**D♭ major**

**G♭ major**

**C♭ major**

# Major Arpeggio

G major

D major

A major

E major

B major

F♯ major

C♯ major

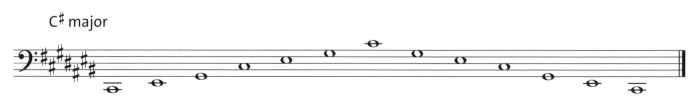

C major

F major

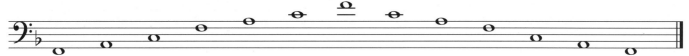

B♭ major

E♭ major

A♭ major

D♭ major

G♭ major

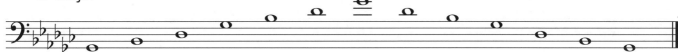

C♭ major

# Major Mode

C ionian

D dorian

E phrygian

F lydian

G mixolydian

A aeolian

B locrian

# Major Mode

### C ionian

### D dorian

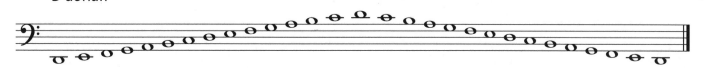

### E phrygian

### F lydian

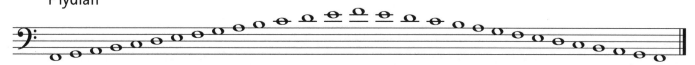

### G mixolydian

### A aeolian

### B locrian

# Melodic Minor Scale

E melodic minor

B melodic minor

F♯ melodic minor

C♯ melodic minor

G♯ melodic minor

D♯ melodic minor

A♯ melodic minor

## A melodic minor

## D melodic minor

## G melodic minor

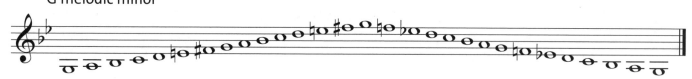

## C melodic minor

## F melodic minor

## B♭ melodic minor

## E♭ melodic minor

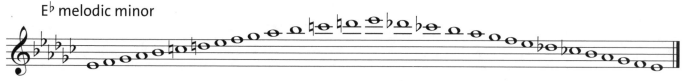

## A♭ melodic minor

# Harmonic Minor Scale

### E harmonic minor

### B harmonic minor

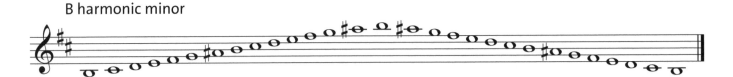

### F♯ harmonic minor

### C♯ harmonic minor

### G♯ harmonic minor

### D♯ harmonic minor

### A♯ harmonic minor

## A harmonic minor

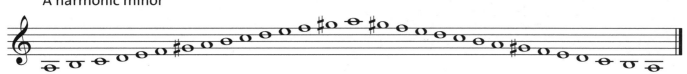

## D harmonic minor

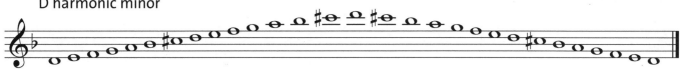

## G harmonic minor

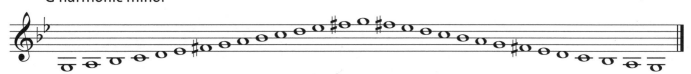

## C harmonic minor

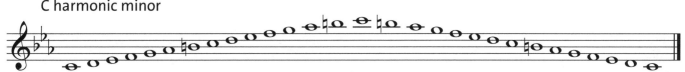

## F harmonic minor

## B♭ harmonic minor

## E♭ harmonic minor

## A♭ harmonic minor

# Minor Arpeggio

E minor

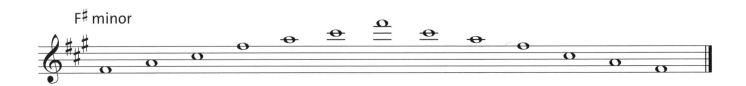

B minor

F# minor

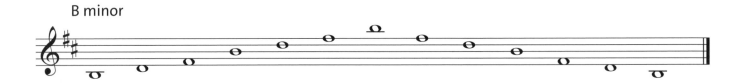

C# minor

G# minor

D# minor

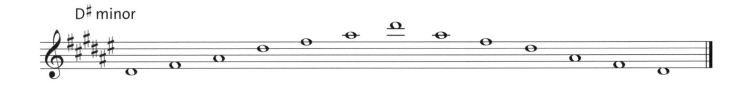

A# minor

**A minor**

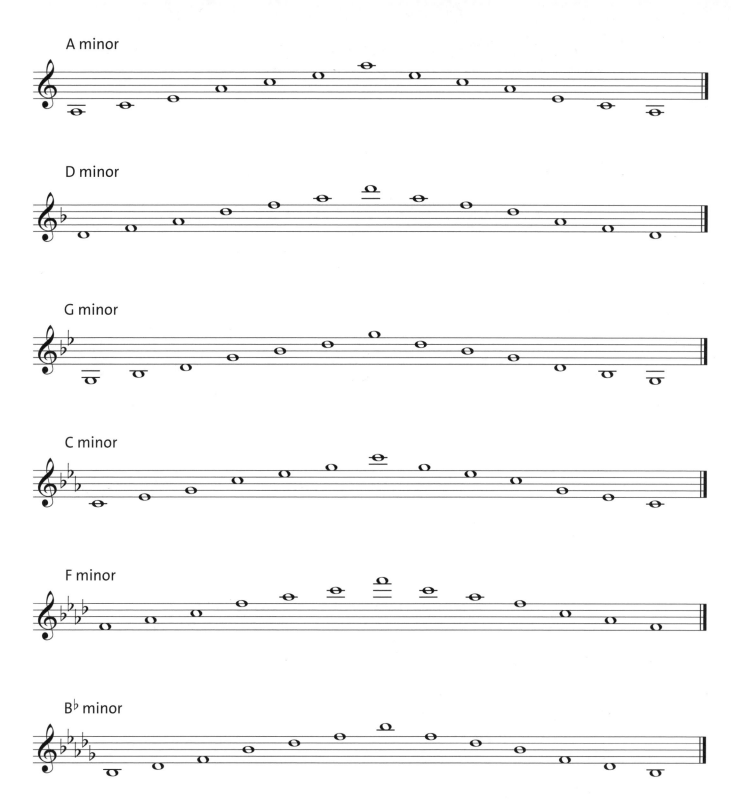

**D minor**

**G minor**

**C minor**

**F minor**

**B♭ minor**

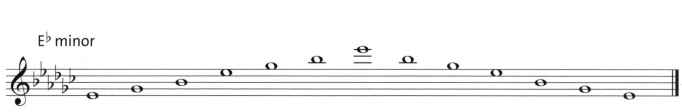

**E♭ minor**

**A♭ minor**

# Melodic Minor Scale

E melodic minor

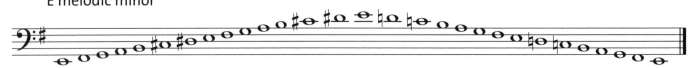

B melodic minor

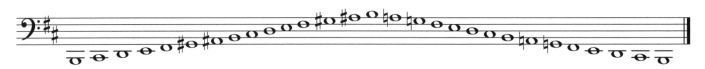

F# melodic minor

C# melodic minor

G# melodic minor

D# melodic minor

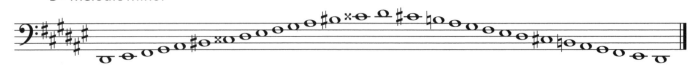

A# melodic minor

**A melodic minor**

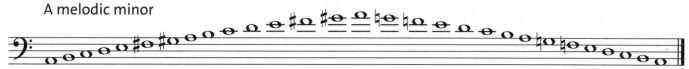

**D melodic minor**

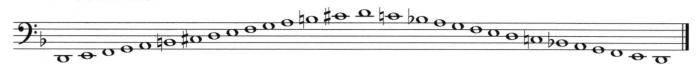

**G melodic minor**

**C melodic minor**

**F melodic minor**

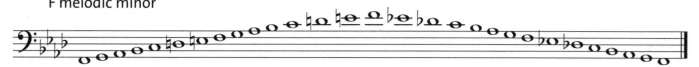

**B♭ melodic minor**

**E♭ melodic minor**

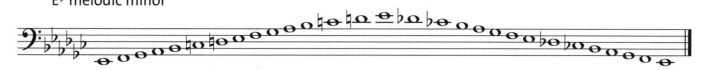

**A♭ melodic minor**

# Harmonic Minor Scale

E harmonic minor

B harmonic minor

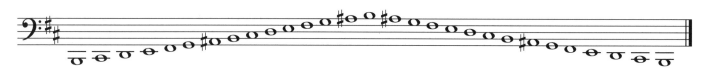

F♯ harmonic minor

C♯ harmonic minor

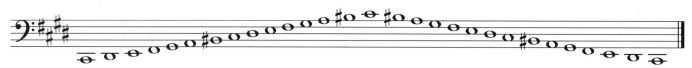

G♯ harmonic minor

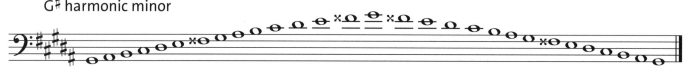

D♯ harmonic minor

A♯ harmonic minor

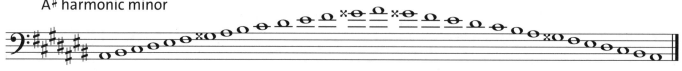

**A harmonic minor**

**D harmonic minor**

**G harmonic minor**

**C harmonic minor**

**F harmonic minor**

**B♭ harmonic minor**

**E♭ harmonic minor**

**A♭ harmonic minor**

# Minor Arpeggio

E minor

B minor

F# minor

C# minor

G# minor

D# minor

A# minor

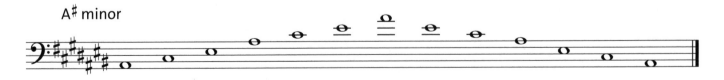

**A minor**

**D minor**

**G minor**

**C minor**

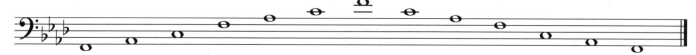

**F minor**

**B♭ minor**

**E♭ minor**

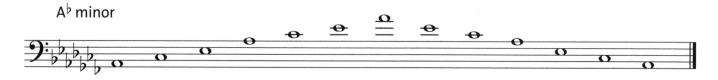

**A♭ minor**

# Major Pentatonic Scale

G major

D major

A major

E major

B major

F# major

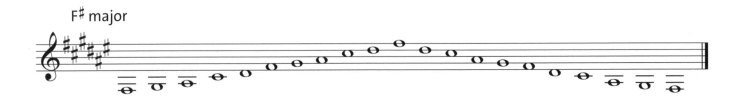

C# major

**C major**

**F major**

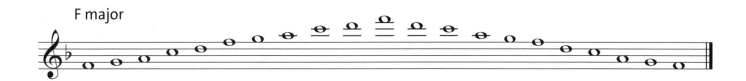

**B♭ major**

**E♭ major**

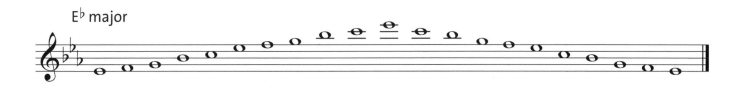

**A♭ major**

**D♭ major**

**G♭ major**

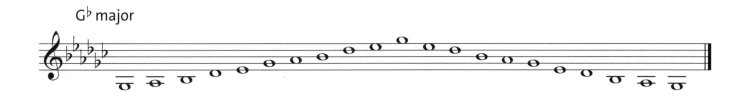

**C♭ major**

# Minor Pentatonic Scale

E minor

B minor

F# minor

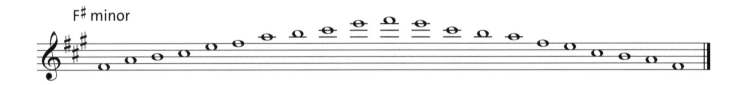

C# minor

G# minor

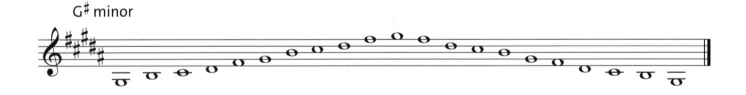

D# minor

A# minor

## A minor

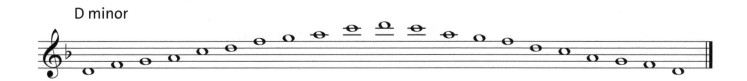

## D minor

## G minor

## C minor

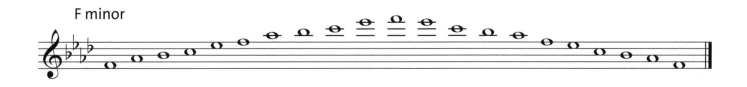

## F minor

## B♭ minor

## E♭ minor

## A♭ minor

# Blues Scale

E blues

B blues

F# blues

C# blues

G# blues

D# blues

A# blues

**A blues**

**D blues**

**G blues**

**C blues**

**F blues**

**B♭ blues**

**E♭ blues**

**A♭ blues**

# Major Pentatonic Scale

G major

D major

A major

E major

B major

F# major

C# major

**C major**

**F major**

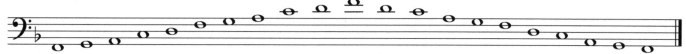

**Bb major**

**Eb major**

**Ab major**

**Db major**

**Gb major**

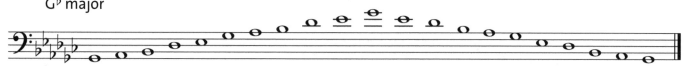

**Cb major**

# Minor Pentatonic Scale

E minor

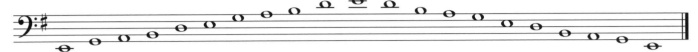

B minor

F# minor

C# minor

G# minor

D# minor

A# minor

**A minor**

**D minor**

**G minor**

**C minor**

**F minor**

**B♭ minor**

**E♭ minor**

**A♭ minor**

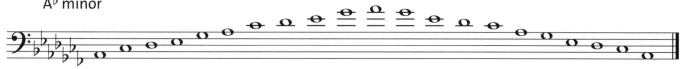

# Blues Scale

E blues

B blues

F# blues

C# blues

G# blues

D# blues

A# blues

## A blues

## D blues

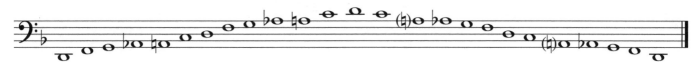

## G blues

## C blues

## F blues

## B♭ blues

## E♭ blues

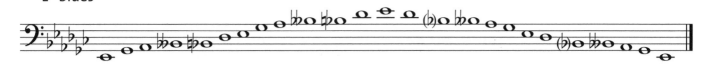

## A♭ blues

# Chromatic and Whole-Tone Scales

**Chromatic**

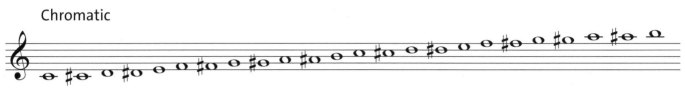

**C whole tone**

**D♭ whole tone**

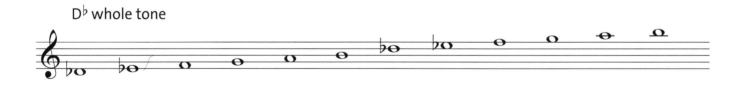

# Diminished Scale

C diminished

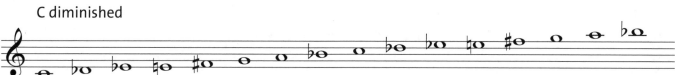

C# diminished

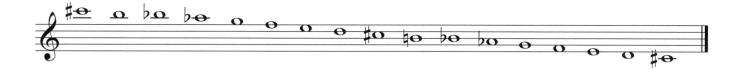

D diminished

# Diminished and Augmented Arpeggios

C diminished 7

D♭ diminished 7

D diminished 7

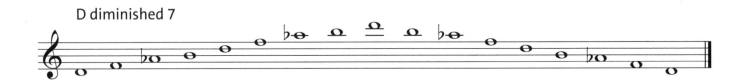

C augmented

D♭ augmented

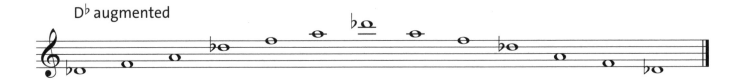

D augmented

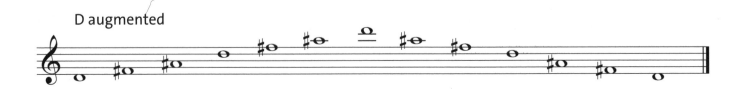

E♭ augmented

# Chromatic and Whole-Tone Scales

**Chromatic**

**C whole tone**

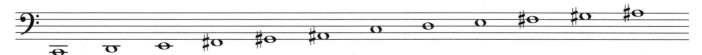

**D♭ whole tone**

# Diminished Scale

### C diminished

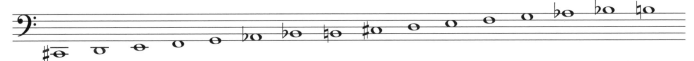

### C# diminished

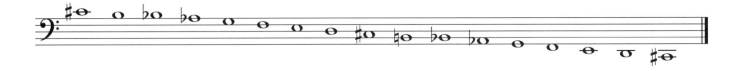

### D diminished

# Diminished and Augmented Arpeggios

C diminished 7

D♭ diminished 7

D diminished 7

C augmented

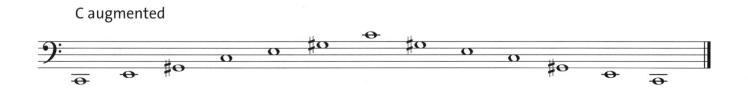

D♭ augmented

D augmented

E♭ augmented

# Minor 7 Arpeggio

A minor 7

E minor 7

B minor 7

F# minor 7

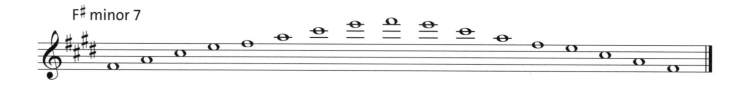

C# minor 7

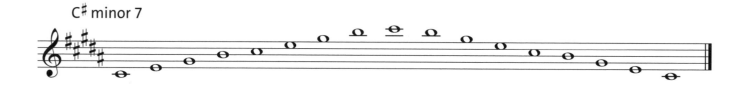

G# minor 7

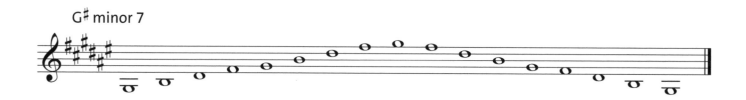

D# minor 7

**D minor 7**

**G minor 7**

**C minor 7**

**F minor 7**

**B♭ minor 7**

**E♭ minor 7**

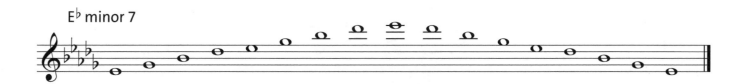

**A♭ minor 7**

**D♭ minor 7**

# Dominant 7 Arpeggio

D dominant 7

A dominant 7

E dominant 7

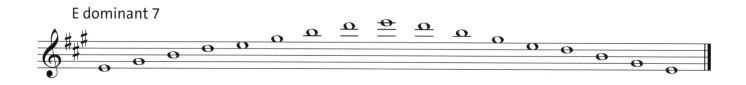

B dominant 7

F# dominant 7

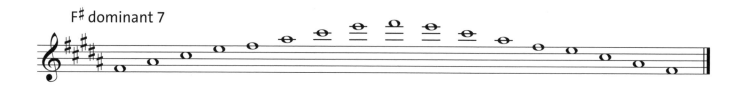

C# dominant 7

G# dominant 7

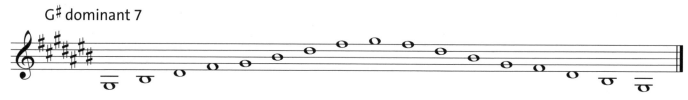

**G dominant 7**

**C dominant 7**

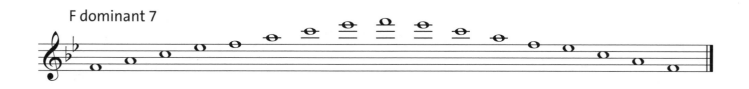

**F dominant 7**

**B♭ dominant 7**

**E♭ dominant 7**

**A♭ dominant 7**

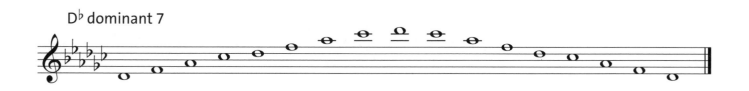

**D♭ dominant 7**

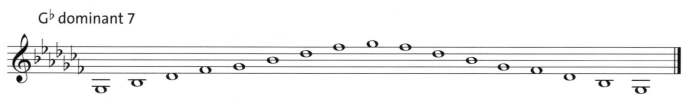

**G♭ dominant 7**

# Minor 7 Arpeggio

A minor 7

E minor 7

B minor 7

F# minor 7

C# minor 7

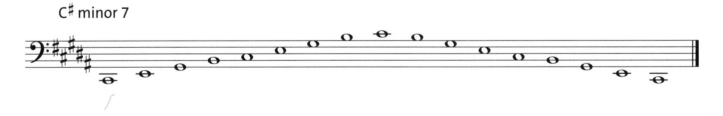

G# minor 7

D# minor 7

**D minor 7**

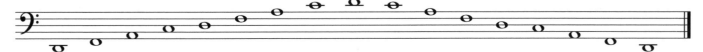

**G minor 7**

**C minor 7**

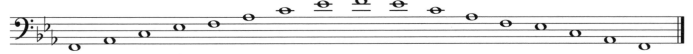

**F minor 7**

**B♭ minor 7**

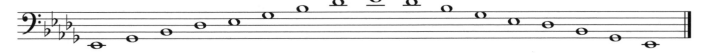

**E♭ minor 7**

**A♭ minor 7**

**D♭ minor 7**

# Dominant 7 Arpeggio

D dominant 7

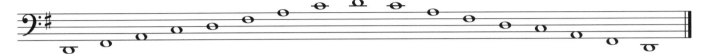

A dominant 7

E dominant 7

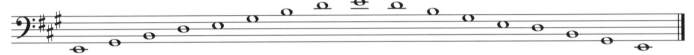

B dominant 7

F# dominant 7

C# dominant 7

G# dominant 7

## G dominant 7

## C dominant 7

## F dominant 7

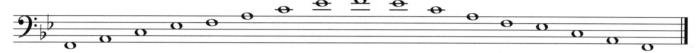

## B♭ dominant 7

## E♭ dominant 7

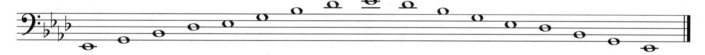

## A♭ dominant 7

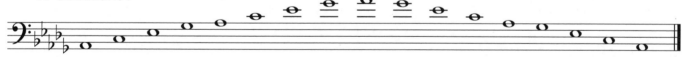

## D♭ dominant 7

## G♭ dominant 7

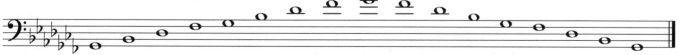

# Practice Tips

Finding new and challenging ways to play scales and arpeggios is a great way to improve technique, memory and theoretical knowledge. Here are some ways to get the most out of your practice session.

Be sure to play the whole exercise at a constant tempo – don't just slow down for the hard bits. Go over the parts you find tricky until they are good and smooth, and then try the whole exercise. There's nothing to be gained from playing an exercise quickly if you can't play it properly at a slower tempo. Sometimes it's tempting to play tricky passages quickly simply because when you do, the mistakes don't last as long!

Once you are happy with the way you play a scale up and down, try skipping notes, leapfrog fashion, as below. This scale is set out in thirds. The slurs have been added just to show how the notes are grouped, but you can try any articulation you like:

## Exercise 1:

You could also try jumping in fourths, or fifths, like this:

## Exercise 2:

Another very common way to play a scale is to run up three notes, back one, then up three, and so on:

## Exercise 3:

When you start jumping more than one step at a time, the line between scales and arpeggios becomes blurred. Look at the following example. Here, the second and fourth notes are omitted, then the pattern repeats starting on the second note, and then on the third note, and so on. In reality this is a series of arpeggios on the modes of the major scale.

## Exercise 4:

And, of course, you could play up one group and come down the next group, like this:

## Exercise 5:

For arpeggios, a simple variation is to leapfrog like this – it can sound very grand:

## Exercise 6:

For pentatonic scales, try running down the scale from the top in staggered groups of three. You will hear this kind of sound played by funky horn sections. Here is an example for a minor pentatonic scale:

## Exercise 7:

If you try this with the blues scale it'll sound really authentic:

## Exercise 8:

Rhythmic groupings can provide lots of variety and interest. Try this simple exercise:

## Exercise 9:

Now play it with a dotted rhythm. Can you play it accurately? Could you play it with the dotted rhythm reversed?

## Exercise 10:

Here's a fun way to play an arpeggio: if you are near a piano, put your foot on the sustain pedal and play the arpeggio on your instrument. Can you hear it ring on?

In a one-octave scale, five groups of triplets work perfectly. Once you are familiar with a scale in every key you could try linking chromatically between keys:

## Exercise 11:

Finally, here are a couple of ideas for the minor 7 and dominant 7 arpeggios. Try practising the dominant 7 arpeggios in a sequence. Ask your teacher to show you the circle of fifths, and arrange the dominant 7 arpeggios in order. You will find that one leads to the other:

## Exercise 12:

Try playing the minor 7 arpeggio, followed by the dominant 7 arpeggio in the same key. This sort of exercise becomes very useful in jazz.

## Exercise 13:

You don't have to play these arpeggios starting with the root note each time. In the previous exercise the dominant 7 arpeggios started on the 3rd, which helps the exercise to flow.

You can find new combinations and patterns by experimenting yourself. Good luck!

> You can begin any scale at any point.
> Try starting on the lowest note of your instrument, or try starting on the highest note you know.
>
> You don't have to play a whole octave, either, and you could extend to any number of notes.
>
> When you're playing a piece, you will rarely come across an entire scale but you will very often find fragments to play, so try doing the same in your scale practice.

123456789